postman P

ANNUAL 199

Written by Brenda Apsley
Illustrated by Ray and Christine Mutimer
Design by Traffika Publishing Limited

POSTMAN PAT © Woodland Animations Limited 1998.
Licensed by Copyrights. All rights reserved.

Published in Great Britain in 1998 by
World International Limited,
Deanway Technology Centre,
Wilmslow Road, Handforth,
Cheshire SK9 3FB.

Printed in Italy
ISBN 0 7498 3770 5

£5.50
UK only

CONTENTS

Hello! Welcome to my new 1999 Annual. Inside there are lots of stories that are fun to read. Find out what happened when I made pancakes with Julian, and when Julian tried to forecast the weather. Read about the fun everyone in the village had at the Greendale Conker Competition, and how Jess got lost – but not for long! There are lots of puzzles, games and things to make and do, too. But first, turn the page to read the first story, about my good idea – and lots of little yellow plastic ducks!

Quackers!

Postman Pat starts work very early in the morning. He is usually out delivering the post when the other people in Greendale are still fast asleep.

Sam Waldron is someone else who starts work early. He has to get his mobile shop ready for his first customers.

One morning Pat saw Sam getting his mobile shop ready and stopped to say hello. "I've been to the market to buy fresh vegetables," said Sam. "I need to keep the shop stocked with all the things people want." But when he opened the back door to put the vegetables inside, lots and lots of little yellow plastic ducks fell out! There were hundreds of them all over the road.

"I didn't know you sold plastic ducks!" said Pat.

6

"I don't," said Sam. "I'm selling some new crackers called Quackers Crackers. The ones with little ducks on the packet. The people who make them keep sending me these little plastic ducks. It seems a shame to throw them away. But if I don't get rid of them I won't have any space for anything else in the shop. What can I do with them? Any ideas, Pat?"

"You could put them in your bath!" laughed Pat. "But I don't think there would be room for you if you did!"

Pat helped Sam to put the ducks in some empty boxes and set off again on his round.

Later that morning Pat met the Reverend Timms. He was looking up at the church tower. "The stone work needs cleaning," said the vicar. "But the work costs a lot of money. We need to do some fund raising. We've had a jumble sale and a cake stall. I think we need to come up with a new idea.

Something that everyone will really enjoy. Any ideas, Pat?"

"That's the second time I've been asked that today!" said Pat, thinking about Sam and his van full of little plastic ducks. They gave Pat an idea. "We could have a duck race," said Pat. "It will be fun for everyone – and we'll raise some money to help pay for the cleaning of the tower."

"A duck race sounds a good idea," said the Reverend Timms. "But where will you get the ducks from? I don't think the ones on the village pond would like racing!"

"You leave the ducks to me, Vicar," said Pat. "I know just where to find them. Hundreds of them!"

Pat had a busy time organising the duck race. He and Julian made posters and put them up all over Greendale. Sam Waldron took the boxes of ducks to Pat's house.

8

On Saturday morning Pat sat at a table near the old bridge in Greendale. Beside him were the boxes of little yellow plastic ducks. The villagers all came to join in the fun. They bought all the ducks. Each one cost enough money to clean one stone of the church tower.

Pat explained about the race. "Choose your own ducks. Write your name on the base of each one, then set them on the river behind the starting line. The Reverend Timms will start the race. The first duck to reach the finishing line on the village green is the winner."

Soon the big boxes were empty and hundreds of little yellow ducks bobbed around on the river. Julian and Charlie Pringle held a rope across the river to stop them setting off too soon.

When everything was ready, Pat ran off down the course so that he could be at the finishing line when the first duck got there.

"Ready, get set, GO!" said the Reverend Timms. Julian and Charlie lifted the rope and off raced the little ducks. The river carried them along quite quickly, and soon the river was a mass of bobbing yellow ducks. Their owners cheered them on from the bank.

"Faster! Faster! Faster!" said Tom Pottage.

"I hope my little duck wins," said his sister, Katy.

Pat and Sara were waiting on the village green as the first ducks bobbed along the river towards them. They held a pink ribbon for the finishing line.

Soon lots more ducks and their owners arrived, hurrying along the riverside path.

There was a big cheer and everyone clapped as the first little duck crossed the finishing line. Pat fished it out of the water with Julian's old fishing net. He looked at the name written on the bottom. "The winner of the Greendale Duck Race is..." said Pat, "...Katy Pottage!"

Katy stepped forward and gave her duck a little hug. The Reverend Timms gave her a little gold cup. "Well done, Katy," he said.

"You can take your duck home with you, Katy," said Pat. "Have you got a name for it?"

"I don't know," said Katy. "Any ideas, Postman Pat?"

"This is where I came in!" laughed Pat. "How about Quackers?"

"That's just the right name for my little duck," said Katy. "Well done, Quackers!"

11

Read with Postman Pat

Can you read the story of the Duck Race?
The little pictures will help you.

 has a problem. The church

needs cleaning. But the work costs a lot of

 . "How can we collect money and

have fun at the same time?" he asks  .

Pat thinks about  . He has lots of

little  in his  . "Let's have a

Duck Race," says Pat.

Pat sits at a and sells ducks. People

use a  to write their 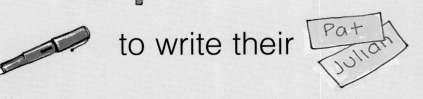 on them.

12

 and Charlie hold  across the river.

The race starts. The little ducks bob along the

Pat waits with  on the village green.

They hold a  across the river.

Pat uses a to scoop up the first duck.

"The winner is ," says Pat.

Reverend Timms gives her a .

"Well done, Katy!" he says.

A Quacking Good Card to Make

The Duck Race was fun. I'll show you how to make a duck card with a beak that opens. It makes a good birthday card.

you will need:
piece of A4 paper
safety scissors
felt-tip pens
ruler
pencil

1 Lay the paper flat. Fold the card in half so that the long edges are together.

2 Ask a grown-up to help you make a cut across the folded edge. It should be 7cm from the top and 6cm wide

3 With the paper still folded, measure 6cm up and 6cm down along the fold. Start measuring from the place where your cut began. Make a mark at each point with your pencil.

4 With your pencil and ruler draw a line from each point to the end of the cut. Then turn your paper over and do the same there. Can you see which shape you have drawn?

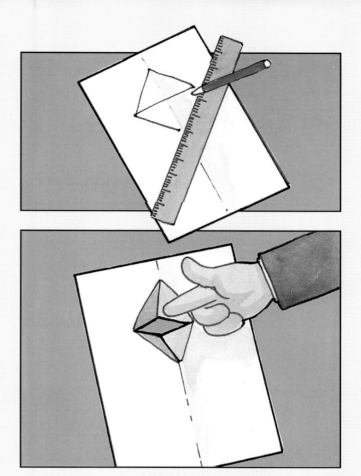

5 Now put your finger at the place where the cut meets the fold. Gently push each flap through to the other side, folding along your pencil lines. This makes your duck's 'beak'.

6 Turn your paper round so that the 'beak' is at the bottom.

7 Now fold the paper the other way, so that the short sides meet. Make sure that you fold your paper so that the 'beak' is not covered up.

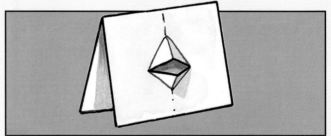

Now for the fun part.
Draw a duck head around the beak.
Colour it. Write a message on the front of your card.

Have a quacking good birthday!

15

Things to See in Greendale

It's the school holidays. Julian and his friends are bored. "There's nothing to do," says Julian.

"There's LOTS to do!" says Pat. He gives each of the children a sheet of paper with little pictures and boxes on it. "There's a list of things to see in Greendale. Can you find them all before teatime?"

Help Julian and his friends find the things on Pat's list. Put a tick in each circle when you find them in the picture.

Did you enjoy the puzzle?
There is another one on page 44.

Pancake Day

1. One morning Julian looks at the calendar. "It's Shrove Tuesday, Dad," he says. "Can we make pancakes?" Pat says yes. He loves them!

2. Pat and Julian mix eggs, milk and flour in a bowl. It's messy work. They are soon covered in spots of batter. Pat even has one on the end of his nose!

3. Pat pours some batter into a frying pan. It soon cooks. "Now for the fun part," he says. "Tossing the pancake. Stand back and watch an expert!"

4. Pat tosses the pancake up into the air. It flips over and comes down again. Pat catches it in the frying pan. "Great, Dad," says Julian. "What a catch!"

5. "I'm getting good at this," he says. Pat makes more pancakes and tosses each one a bit higher into the air. "Up you go!" he says.

6. Pat lets Julian pour batter into the pan. "Now for a high toss!" he says. Up, up, up, goes the pancake, high into the air. But it doesn't come down again!

7. "Where's it gone?" asks Julian. Pat is having too much fun to look for it. "Don't worry about it," says Pat. "There's lots of batter left. I'll make another."

8. Pat cooks another pancake. "This time I'm going to do a super-high toss, with two flips," he says. "It's like the Pancake Olympics!" says Julian.

9. Pat tosses the pancake high into the air. It flips once, twice. Pat waits for it to come down and land in the frying pan. But the pancake doesn't come down!

10. "It doesn't matter," says Pat, and he makes another one. This time he tries a back flip. Can you guess what happens? Yes, that pancake disappears, too!

11. A little while later Sara comes in. Julian and Pat are covered in batter. So is the kitchen. It looks messy. Very messy. "What have you been up to?" asks Sara.

12. Sara is expecting lots of pancakes for tea. But there are only three. "Where are the rest?" she asks. Pat wipes a blob of batter off his nose. He has some explaining to do!

Pat's pancakes ended up in some very odd places!
Can you find six of them?

The answer is on page 6I.

Hunt the Pancakes

Hunt the Pancakes is a fun game to play with a friend. This is how to make the game:

• Using a pencil and ruler, copy out two grids like the one below, one for each player.

• Number the boxes across the top from left to right, I 2 3 4 5. Label the boxes down the side from top to bottom, a b c d e.

This is how to play the game:

• Each player draws 5 pancakes on his or her sheet of paper, one per square. Don't let the other person see where you draw them.

• You have to find out where your friend's pancakes are. Take turns to choose a number and a letter. Follow the number down with your finger. Follow the letter across. Where they meet is the box you have chosen. To show you how, the pancakes in the grid on this page are in boxes 3a, 2d, 5e, Ic and 4b.

• When you guess a box with one of your friend's pancakes in it, they have to cross it out.

• The first player to find all 5 of his or her friend's pancakes is the winner.

	1	2	3	4	5
a			🥞		
b				🥞	
c	🥞				
d		🥞			
e					🥞

22

Postman Pat's Post Code Puzzle

Do you know your post code? Post codes are special sets of letters and numbers that are part of your address. Every address has a post code. They help machines to sort the letters so that postmen like me can deliver post to the right addresses.

Write your name and address on this envelope. The bottom line is for your post code. Ask a grown-up to help you if you are not sure.

The letter or letters at the start of the post code show which town or city you live in. The rest of the letters and numbers show which road or street you live on.

Can you draw lines to match the post code letters to the names of the towns and cities?

B	MANCHESTER
CF	YORK
M	BIRMINGHAM
YO	GLASGOW
G	LIVERPOOL
L	CARDIFF

The answers are on page 61.

Message in a Bottle

Trader Jones had a problem. Charlie Chalk and all the others who live on the island of Merrytwit always take their empty coconut milk bottles back to his store, so that Trader can recycle them. But for the last few mornings there had been no empty bottles for Trader to wash and use again.

"Have you been returning your empty coconut milk bottles?" Trader asked Charlie one morning.

"Of course I have," said Charlie. "I left three outside the store last night."

"Well, they're not there now," said Trader. "And neither are the ones that Captain Mildred, Lewis T. Duck and Mary the Hover Fairy left last night. I don't know what's happening to them."

"There's only one way to find out," said Charlie. "We'll hide in the coconut trees tonight and see who's taking them. I'll come back as soon as it's dark."

That night, Trader and Charlie sat under the coconut trees at the side of the store and waited. They held large leaves over their heads so they wouldn't be seen.

They waited and waited. They waited for most of the night. The moon came out, and the black sky was dotted with stars. Still they waited.

After hours of sitting on the hard ground Trader Jones was getting stiff, and starting to feel cold. He was just about to suggest that they went into the store for an early breakfast when Charlie put his finger to his lips and pointed.

Trader looked hard. There, on the edge of the clearing, he saw a movement. Just then the moon moved from behind a cloud and shone on – Edward!

Edward looked this way and that, then he crept towards Trader's store – and took the four milk bottles that Charlie and Trader had put out as bait.

When Edward had gone away Trader and Charlie came out of their hiding place. "What does Edward want with empty coconut milk bottles?" Trader whispered.

"Let's follow him and find out," Charlie whispered back, and they crept off through the trees.

Lewis knew just what Edward was doing. "Edward wants a pen friend," he explained. "He's writing messages and putting them in bottles. He's hoping that the sea will take them far away and that someone will write back to him."

"But the currents in the sea around the island won't take the bottles far enough away," said Trader, who knows about these things. "They'll never reach land."

"And if Edward keeps throwing bottles into the sea we'll have none left to put our coconut milk in," said Charlie. "We've got to stop him somehow."

Trader and Charlie followed Edward. It was starting to get light when he stopped near a large flat rock at the headland on the edge of the sea. They watched as he wrote on four pieces of paper and put one piece into each of the bottles. Then Edward went to the edge of the rocks and threw the bottles into the sea.

Charlie and Trader went back to the store before Edward saw them. It was very puzzling. They were trying to work out what Edward was up to when Lewis T. Duck came into the store. "We've just seen Edward throwing coconut bottles into the sea," said Charlie. "Any idea what he's up to?"

"Poor Edward," said Lewis. "He is really looking forward to getting a letter."

Later, Charlie and Trader went to the headland again. They used fishing nets to haul in all the bottles that bobbed around in the sea.

Trader loaded the bottles on to his truck to take back to the store, but Charlie kept one. He had an idea.

Next morning Edward rushed to Charlie's caravan waving a piece of paper. He had a big smile on his face. He looked really pleased. "Guess what?" he said to Charlie. "I've been sending messages in bottles to try to find a penfriend. This morning I found a bottle on the beach. There's a message inside it, and it's addressed to me. Look!"

"To Edward," Charlie read aloud. "Merrytwit Island. Who's it from?"

Edward opened the piece of paper and read the letter. "It's from Neptune, the King of the Sea!" Edward told Charlie. "He says he's very pleased to meet me and will write to me from time to time, but right now he needs my help. Can I help stop people putting empty coconut milk bottles into the water? They're polluting the sea."

Charlie smiled. It was good to see Edward looking so happy with his letter. "And do you think you can help stop coconut milk bottles getting into the sea, Edward?" he asked.

Edward smiled a little smile. "I think I can, Charlie," he said. "I think I can."

The Conker King of Greendale

It was October. Cold winter winds were starting to blow, and the leaves were turning from green to brown. Some of the leaves had already fallen to the ground and lay like a crunchy carpet on the grass of the village green.

Pat was driving home one afternoon when he saw Julian and Charlie Pringle on the village green. They were scuffling around among the leaves with their feet. "Hello, you two," said Pat. "What are you doing?"

"We're looking for conkers," said Julian. "They're starting to fall from the horse chestnut trees."

"When we've collected some we're going to make them hard and thread them on to strings," said Charlie. "Then we can play conkers with them."

"I used to love playing conkers when I was your age," said Pat. "I was the Conker King of Greendale one year."

Pat explained that every autumn all the people in the village used to take part in a contest to find the Conker King. "We haven't had a contest for years," he said. "But we could start it up again. What do you think?"

"Great idea!" said Charlie.

"Ace!" said Julian.

Pat told everyone about the contest when he was out on his rounds. Soon the whole village was busy collecting conkers. They all had their own ideas about how to make the conkers so hard that they would beat all the others.

Miss Hubbard baked hers in the oven to harden them.

Ted Glen soaked his in salt water.

The Reverend Timms soaked his in vinegar.

Peter Fogg wouldn't say what he did to harden his conkers. "It's a secret family recipe," he told Pat.

29

On the day of the contest everyone met up on the village green. There were lots of matches. Pat was the referee. The winners of the first round went on to the second round, and so on, until there were just four people left.

In the first semi-final Granny Dryden's conker split Sam Waldron's best one. In the second semi-final Mrs Goggins conker beat Major Forbes champion. Now Granny Dryden and Mrs Goggins conkers were both tenners, which meant that they had beaten ten others.

"It's time for the grand final," Pat announced, "between Granny Dryden and Mrs Goggins. Good luck. You've done well to reach the final," he told them both.

"Well, we are the oldest people in the village, you know," said Granny Dryden. "I played conkers all the time when I was a girl."

"So did I," said Mrs Goggins. "We've both had years and years of practice, so we should be good, shouldn't we?"

The final of the conker contest was exciting. Granny Dryden swung her conker as hard as she could, but it would not break Mrs Goggins. Mrs Goggins swung her conker just as hard, but it would not break Granny Dryden's. Both the conkers were champions.

Pat decided that the only fair result would be a draw. He had a rosette for each of them. "I now declare that this year's winners are Granny Dryden and Mrs Goggins," he said. "But you're not the Conker Kings of Greendale."

"Why not?" asked Granny Dryden.

"Yes, why not?" said Mrs Goggins.

Pat smiled as he pinned the rosettes on them. "Well, two ladies can't be Conker Kings of Greendale, can they?" he said. "So congratulations not to the Conker Kings of Greendale, but to the Conker QUEENS! Well done!"

Count the Conkers

There were lots of conkers lying on the ground after the contest. It was Julian and Charlie's job to pick them all up. How many conkers can you count in the picture?

Smile, Please!

Pat took his camera to the Conker Contest.
He took photographs of the winners.
"Smile, please!" he said.

Here are two of the pictures Pat took. They
look alike, but there are five things that are
different in the second picture. Can you find
them all?

The answers are on page 6l.

Jess's Purrfect Day

Out in All Weathers

1. Julian is learning about the weather at school. His class have been busy watching the weather and making notes about it.

2. Julian has been busy at home, too. He has made some equipment to measure the weather and do tests. He has set it up in the garden.

3. "Now I can tell you what the weather is going to be like," he tells Pat. "You won't be caught in a shower of rain or wearing the wrong clothes."

4. "There are lots of old sayings about telling what the weather is going to be like," Pat tells Julian. 'Red sky at night, shepherd's delight' is one of them."

5. "In other words, a red sky at night means the next day will be fine," Pat explains. "'Red sky at morning, shepherd's warning' means bad weather."

6. Julian writes down the amount of rain he has collected in a jam jar. "I think I'll stick to working it out the scientific way, Dad," he says.

7. Next morning Pat is setting off for work when Julian runs after him. "I'm sure it's going to rain today," he says. "Take this umbrella with you, Dad."

8. Julian has Pat's big waterproof coat, too. "I think the rain might be heavy, so you'll need this," he says. "Thanks, Julian," says Pat. "Is that everything?"

9. Julian looks at his weather station. "Nearly," he says. "But if the rain is extra heavy the roads might flood, so don't forget your wellington boots."

10. Pat puts the umbrella and coat and wellington boots into his van. "If I take more stuff with me there'll be no room for the post!" laughs Pat.

11. Pat gets into the van and is just about to drive off when Julian stops him. He gives Pat his long woolly winter scarf and warm mittens.

12. "It may turn cold after lunch, Dad," says Julian. "So you'll need these." Pat looks up at the blue sky. "If you say so," he says. "Can I get off to work now?"

13. Julian looks in his note book. "In a minute," he says, and runs back into the house. He comes out with sunglasses and sun cream. "You may need these."

14. Pat puts the rest of the things on the seat beside him. There's hardly enough room for Jess. "See you later," says Pat, and he drives off to do his deliveries.

15. When Pat comes home Julian is waiting for him at the garden gate. "Well, Dad, did the weather turn out as I told you it would?" he asks.

16. Pat struggles out of the van carrying his umbrella, wellington boots, big waterproof coat, winter scarf, woolly mittens, sunglasses and sun cream.

17. "Not quite!" laughs Pat. "There was no rain, no cold snap, no bright sunshine. But there was the one kind of weather you didn't predict – high winds."

18. "A gust of wind blew my cap off and it landed in the duck pond on the village green!" laughs Pat, giving Julian his wet cap. "Sorry, Dad," said Julian.

19. "That's all right," said Pat. "I wore the wellington boots to wade into the pond. And I used the umbrella handle to fish out my cap."

20. Julian is disappointed. He starts to take down his windmill. "Don't get rid of it, son," says Pat. "It's just the thing for drying off my wet cap!"

A Weather Clock to Make

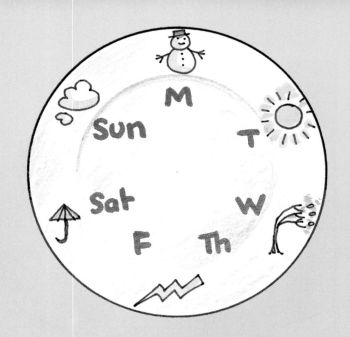

Recording the weather can be fun. Why not make this weather clock and keep a record of the weather each day of the week? Ask a grown-up to help you.

You will need:
paper plate
card
paper fastener
felt tip pens

1. Draw little weather pictures around the side of the paper plate. Try to space them evenly.

Draw:
(snowman)	snow
(sun face)	sun
(bendy tree)	wind
(lightning)	storm
(umbrella)	rain
(clouds)	cloudy

2. Write letters for each day of the week around the middle of the plate. Space them evenly.

Write:
M	Monday
T	Tuesday
W	Wednesday
Th	Thursday
F	Friday
Sat	Saturday
Sun	Sunday

3. Cut out a piece of card 15cm long and 3cm deep. Write **weather** on it.

4. Cut out another piece of card 10cm long and 3cm deep. Write **day** on it.

5. Ask a grown-up to push a paper fastener through the ends of the pieces of card and through the centre of the paper plate. They should look like the hands on a clock.

Each day, move one hand to point to the day, and the other to point to the kind of weather it is, like this.

20 SUPER Postman Pat™
PRIZES TO BE WON!!!

Would you like to own one of these great Postman Pat toys?
You can, if you are one of the lucky winners in this year's
Postman Pat Annual competition!

All you have to do is to answer this question:

What village does Postman Pat live in?

If you get the answer right, you might be the lucky winner of one
of these prizes, all made by Golden Bear.

10 ### Postman Pat playsets
containing a Postman Pat figure,
a postbox with opening door and
a push-along post van.

10 ### Singing Postman Pat
A huggable Postman Pat with Jess
the Cat. When you squeeze Pat's
tummy he starts to sing!

*Write your entry on a postcard, or on
the back of a sealed envelope. There
are three things you must remember to
tells us:*
1. Your **answer** to the question.
2. Which **prize** you would prefer.
3. Your **name, age** and **address**.

Answer_____
Prize choice_____

My name_____Age_____
Address_____
_____
_____
_____

Send your entry to:
Postman Pat Annual Competition
World International Limited, Deanway Technology Centre, Wilmslow Road,
Handforth, Cheshire, SK9 3FB.

The closing date is **Friday 15th January 1999**

Greendale Friends

Can you find the names of ten
Greendale friends in the word
square? They are spelled out left to
right and top to bottom. Tick each
name when you find it.

S	A	M	W	C	D	V	Y	O	T
P	A	X	U	P	A	T	W	Y	O
A	A	T	E	Z	R	L	S	E	M
J	W	P	J	U	L	I	A	N	P
E	T	E	X	Q	Y	R	I	C	P
S	S	R	T	E	D	R	S	W	E
S	S	K	S	G	Q	T	A	V	T
E	A	A	A	F	R	T	R	C	E
C	H	A	R	L	I	E	A	L	R
I	J	Y	K	A	T	Y	G	M	V

CHARLIE

JESS

JULIAN

KATY

PAT

PETER

SAM

SARA

TED

TOM

The answer is on page 6l.

43

Things to See in Greendale

Julian and his friends enjoyed the spotter sheet Pat made for them so much that they asked for another one – and here it is! Join in the fun by looking at the picture of Greendale Farm and ticking off each thing as you find it.

Greendale Sheep

Katy and Tom are helping Peter Fogg on his farm. They are putting the sheep into pens so that they can have their thick woolly coats cut off.

Who will be first to get 10 sheep in their pen, Katy or Tom?

Play the game with a friend. One of you is Katy, the other Tom.

You need a dice, a pencil and a counter each.

Take turns to throw the dice. Start at the arrow. Move around the track the number shown on the dice. If you throw 2, move 2 spaces, and so on.

When you land on a sheep, shade in or tick one of the 10 sheep pictures in your pen.

The first player to fill in all 10 of his or her sheep is the winner. Go around again if you need to.

Rub out the pencil and play again.

High Seas Adventure

1. It has been a long, hot summer on the island of Merrytwit. Each day is the same as the one before. Charlie and the others are bored.

2. Trader Jones leans on his counter and dreams of far away places. Lewis T. Duck sits on the shore, staring at birds swooping in the cloudless sky.

3. Charlie paces up and down outside his caravan. "Nothing exciting ever happens here," he says. "I want an adventure." So does Edward.

4. Captain Mildred stands on the deck of the Buttercup and looks out to sea. "We need an adventure... An adventure on the high seas!"

5. They paint, polish, scrub and wash until Buttercup is ready. "We'll pull her down to the beach and see how she floats," says Captain Mildred.

6. Soon Buttercup is bobbing around in the bay. "Drop anchor!" cries Captain Mildred. "We'll set off on our great adventure tomorrow!"

7. Mary the Hover Fairy repairs the hammocks they will sleep in. "We'll sleep on board tonight," says Captain Mildred. "To get used to them."

8. Getting into the hammocks is tricky. So is staying in them! But at last Captain Mildred and her crew settle down for their first night on the high seas.

9. Later, a storm blows up. Strong winds bend the trees. The roof of Trader's store rattles and creaks. Big clouds of sand blow along the beach.

10. The sky is black. There is loud thunder and zigzags of lightning. The sea seems to boil. High waves crash and smash against Buttercup.

11. The wind blows the boat first one way, then the other. It tosses her around like a little plastic duck in a bath. She rocks from side to side.

Inside, the hammocks swing from side to side. "Ooh, my poor tummy!" groans Arnold. "Get me off here!" moans Edward. "I feel really ill!"

12. "Your face is a funny green colour," Charlie tells Trader Jones. "So is yours," says Trader. "I'd forgotten how awful it is to feel seasick."

13. The storm rages all night long. By morning everyone is feeling very seasick. Arnold feels dizzy. "Get me to dry land!" he moans.

14. Soon the brave sailors are back on land. They feel dizzy and hold their sore tummies. "I'm going to have my adventure right here," says Charlie.

15. Even Captain Mildred says she is staying on dry land because, "A, I can't go off without a crew and B, I feel ill, too!"

Special Delivery!

When Postman Pat got back to the post office one afternoon after delivering the post, he found Mrs Goggins surrounded by sacks of letters and parcels.

"You're going to have a busy afternoon," she told Pat. "There are all these letters and parcels to take to the sorting office in Pencaster."

Pat loaded the sacks into the van and looked at his watch. "I'll be off now then, Mrs Goggins!" he said. "Bye!"

Pat jumped into the van, put the key into the lock and turned it. The engine made a little coughing noise. Pat turned the key again. This time the engine groaned. Pat tried the key for the third time. This time the engine made no noise at all. "Oh, no, Jess," he said. "The van won't start."

Pat went back into the post office. "That was quick, Pat!" laughed Mrs Goggins. "Have you forgotten something?"

"No," said Pat. "The van has broken down. I'll ring the garage and get them to collect it."

A few minutes later the van had gone off to be mended – and Pat was left with the sacks of post to get to Pencaster.

"I'll have to get it there somehow or other," said Pat. "It's important."

Pat set off to walk to Pencaster, though it was a very long way on foot, and it was hard work carrying heavy sacks.

He hadn't gone very far when he met Julian, who was out on his roller skates. "Do you think those skates would fit me?" asked Pat.

Pat tried them on. They were a bit tight, but not too bad. "Can I borrow them for a while?" he asked Julian.

Soon the post was on its way to Pencaster on skates!

Pat was skating past Miss Hubbard's house when a wheel came off one of the skates and Pat ended up in the hedge. "Whatever are you doing, Pat?" asked Miss Hubbard.

Pat explained. "I have to get these sacks of post to the sorting office, but my van has broken down. I borrowed Julian's skates to get there a bit faster."

"I think I can do better than skates," said Miss Hubbard. "Take my bicycle, Pat. You can return it later."

"Thanks, Miss Hubbard," said Pat. "It'll be just the job."

Pat balanced the sacks on each side of the bicycle and set off along the Pencaster road.

He hadn't gone very far when there was a little pop and a hissing sound. Pat looked down. "Oh, no, the tyre's got a puncture," he said. "And I haven't got anything to repair it with."

Pat was looking at the bicycle when Peter Fogg came along on his tractor. Pat explained what had happened. "I can't take you all the way to Pencaster," said Peter. "But I can give you a lift to the crossroads."

"That's great, Peter!" said Pat, and he loaded the sacks and the bicycle on to the tractor and climbed up to sit beside Peter.

It was a bumpy ride, but it saved Pat's legs, and when he got down at the crossroads Pat was delighted to see Sam Waldron coming along the road in his mobile shop. "Thanks, Peter," said Pat. "I'll ask Sam if he can give me a lift now."

Sam was going towards Pencaster, so Pat put the mail sacks into the back of the van with the groceries and climbed up into the cab. "It's a good job I came along when I did," said Sam. "It would have been hard work carrying those heavy sacks up this hill."

When they had gone a little way further along the road, Sam's van

54

started to make little spluttering noises. It went slower and slower. "What's going on?" said Sam, stopping at the side of the road.

Pat looked at the petrol gauge. The finger pointed to EMPTY. "Look, Sam," he said. "You've run out of petrol!"

"Oh, no," said Sam. "I'll have to walk back all the way to the garage to get some."

"And I'll have to set off again for Pencaster," said Pat.

Pat was sure that he would have to walk all the way to Pencaster now. He was trudging along beside the stone wall that ran around one of Alf Thompson's fields when he heard a voice. "Hello, Pat!" called Alf. "What are you doing up here?"

Pat stopped and peered over the wall. Alf was ploughing the field with one of his big work horses. Pat explained what had happened. "So I'll have to go the rest of the way on foot," he said.

"Oh no you won't," said Alf. "I've got a much better idea. You can go on Major here, my old horse. He's big, but he's as gentle as a lamb. He'll get you and the sacks of mail to Pencaster in no time."

Soon Pat was sitting high up on Major, with the sacks on each side of the horse's broad back. "He'll get you there," said Alf.

He was right. Major seemed to know just where he was going, and soon he and Pat were walking through the streets of Pencaster on the way to the sorting office.

Katy and Tom Pottage were shopping with their mum. "Look!" said Katy. "It's Postman Pat." "He's

delivering the post on a horse!"
said Tom.

Mrs Pottage laughed and waved
to Pat. "That's how it used to be done
in the days before cars and vans were
invented," she said.

When Pat had delivered the post
to the sorting office Major turned for
home and before long Pat was back
at Alf's farm.

"Thank you, Alf. Thank you,
Major," said Pat.

"There's just one problem now,"
said Alf. "How are you going to get
back home?"

"Oh, no," said Pat. "I hadn't
thought about that! I'll just have
to walk."

"I think we can help," said Alf.
"We're driving the pick-up truck and
the trailer into Greendale later."

"But there are only two seats,"
said Pat. "Where will I sit?"

"Wait and see!" said Alf.

Later, Mrs Goggins was very
surprised to see Pat arrive back at
the post office – in a speed boat!
Pat sat in the boat, which was on
Alf's trailer.

"Special delivery for you, Mrs
Goggins!" said Alf.

Jess, Where are You?

1. Julian is sending his aunt a large basket of dried flowers for her birthday. "It's quite fragile," says Pat. "We'll have to pack it carefully."

2. Pat gets a big box from Sam Waldron's mobile shop, straw from Alf Thompson's farm and string and sticky tape from Ted Glen's workshop.

3. Julian and Pat spend ages packing and wrapping and taping the box. It takes a long time. Then Julian writes a label and tapes it in place.

4. Later, Sara calls Jess for his supper But he isn't in the house. Julian looks in the garden, but he isn't there either. Where can he be?

5. Jess is still missing two hours later. Pat looks in the cupboard under the stairs. Julian looks in his wardrobe and in the old toy box. No Jess.

6. Sara looks in the kitchen cupboards. She even looks in the washing machine. Where can Jess be? They start to feel worried about him.

7. Julian looks under the sofa. Then he sees the big parcel. "He couldn't be in there, could he?" he asks. "There's only one way to find out," says Pat.

8. Julian and Pat unwrap the parcel. Off come the tape, paper, label and string. Out comes all the straw and the flowers. But Jess is not in the box.

9. It's time for Julian to go to bed. He doesn't want to go until Jess is found. "You have to be up early for school in the morning," says Sara. "Off you go."

10. "I'll take a torch and look outside," says Pat. "Don't worry, Julian, we'll find him." "I hope so," says Julian, and he says goodnight and goes upstairs.

11. Julian gets undressed and lifts up the lid of the linen basket to put his dirty socks inside when out leaps Jess! Julian picks him up. He purrs happily.

12. Jess has a cheeky look on his face. "Was he stuck, or just hiding?" says Pat. "I don't care," says Julian. "I'm just glad to have him back!"

Sit Still, Jess!

Julian is taking photographs of Jess. "Sit still, Jess!" says Julian. Jess finds it hard to keep still, but he does it in the end. Can you find the two pictures of Jess that are exactly alike?

A

The answer is on page 61.

B

C

D

E

F

G

H

60

Answers to Puzzles

Pancake Day   page 21

Postman Pat's Post Code Puzzle page 23

B = BIRMINGHAM
CF = CARDIFF
M = MANCHESTER
YO = YORK
G = GLASGOW
L = LIVERPOOL

Count the Conkers   page 32
There are 10 conkers on the ground.

Smile, Please!   page 33

Greendale Friends   page 43

S	A	M	W	C	D	V	Y	O	T
P	A	X	U	P	A	T	W	Y	O
A	A	T	E	Z	R	L	S	E	M
J	W	P	J	U	L	I	A	N	P
E	T	E	X	Q	Y	R	I	C	P
S	S	R	T	E	D	R	S	W	E
S	S	K	S	G	Q	T	A	V	T
E	A	D	A	F	R	T	R	C	E
C	H	A	R	L	I	E	A	L	R
I	J	Y	K	A	T	Y	G	M	V

Sit Still, Jess!   page 60
Photographs B and G are the same.